SKID TRAC

Which of these racing cars does not
pass the chequered flag?

MONSTER TRUCKS

Only two of these trucks are exactly the same.
Look carefully to find them.

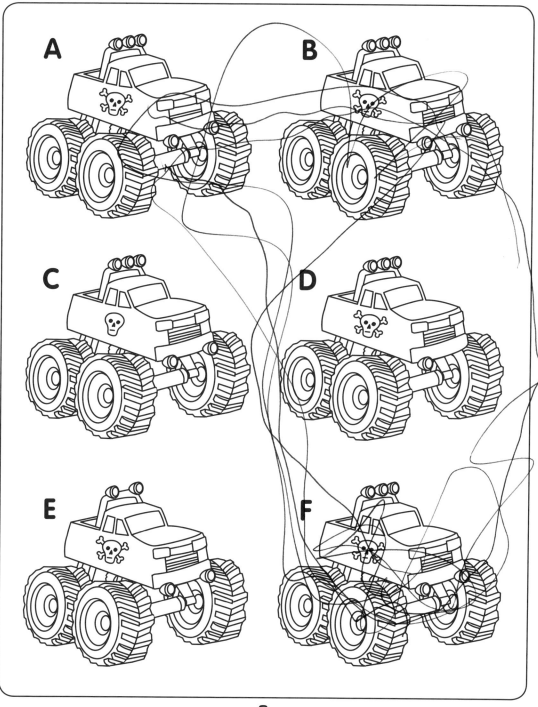

TOP SPEED

Have fun colouring these super-speedy race cars.

MOTORBIKE MATHS

Add up the numbers on each pair of
racing bikes to work out the sums.

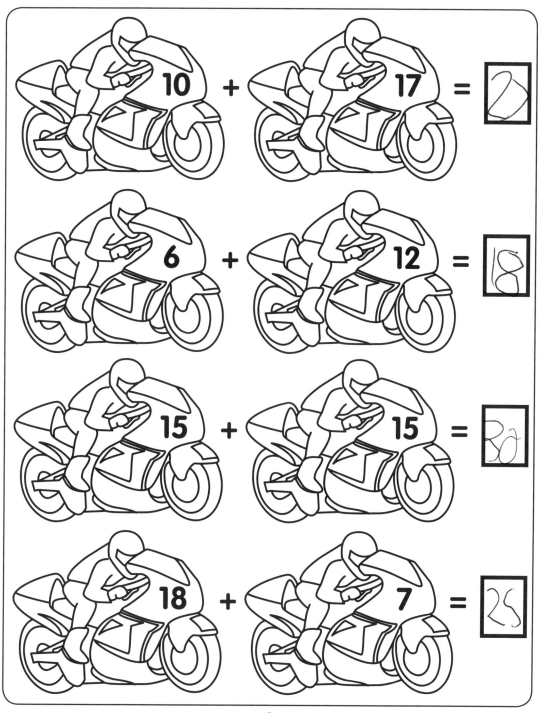

10 + 17 = 27

6 + 12 = 18

15 + 15 = 30

18 + 7 = 25

IT'S A MYSTERY

What load does the tractor need to collect? Cross out any letter that appears twice and use the remaining letters to spell a word.

HARD AT WORK

Colour the tractor with your favourite bright colour.

CAMPING TRIP

Look closely to find four differences between
these two camper vans.

FLY PAST

Have fun colouring these jets and their trails.

SAIL AWAY

Can you find the word SAIL hidden
just once in these letters?

ALL ABOARD

Fill in the missing numbers
to count up in twos.

BLAST OFF!

Start the colouring countdown, this rocket is ready to launch!

SCOOTING OFF!

See if you can find a way to
scoot through the maze.

START

FINISH

SPECIAL DELIVERY

See if you can spot four differences
between these two pictures.

IN A WHIRL

Cross out all the Xs to find something
that helicopters are used for.

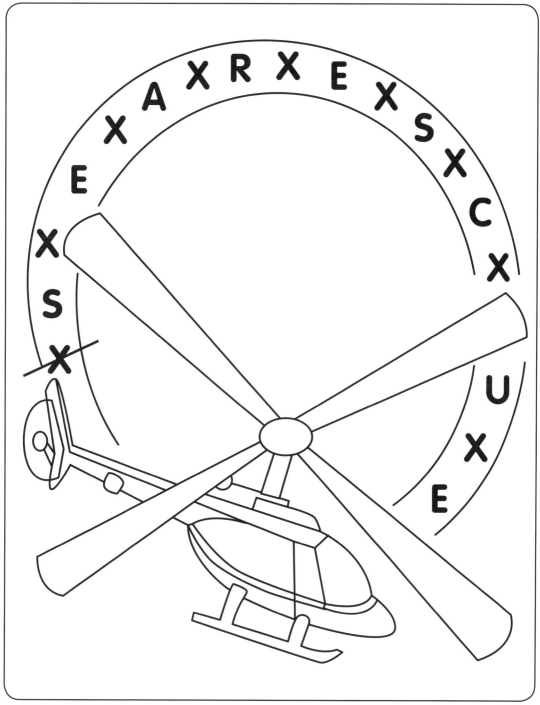

AIR-SEA RESCUE

Add some colour to this dramatic scene!

DARK SIDE OF THE MOON

Which of the silhouettes matches the main
picture of the moon buggy?

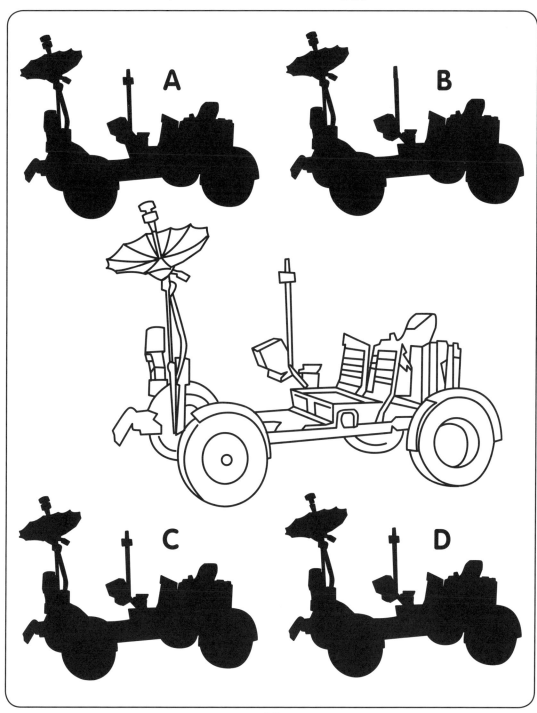

ZOOM-DOKU

Fill in the puzzle so that every row, column and mini-grid has each of the four wheel pictures.

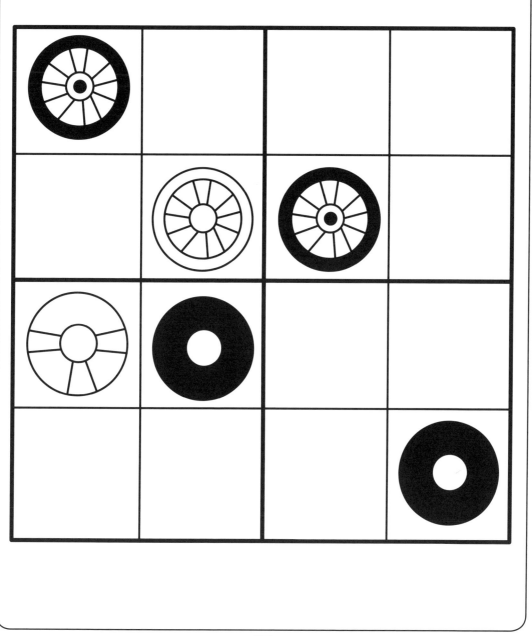

OCEAN LIFE

Colour in this enormous cruise ship!

ROUND AND ROUND

Can you fit each of these car companies into the wheel? The shaded spaces are the last letter of one word and the first letter of the next.

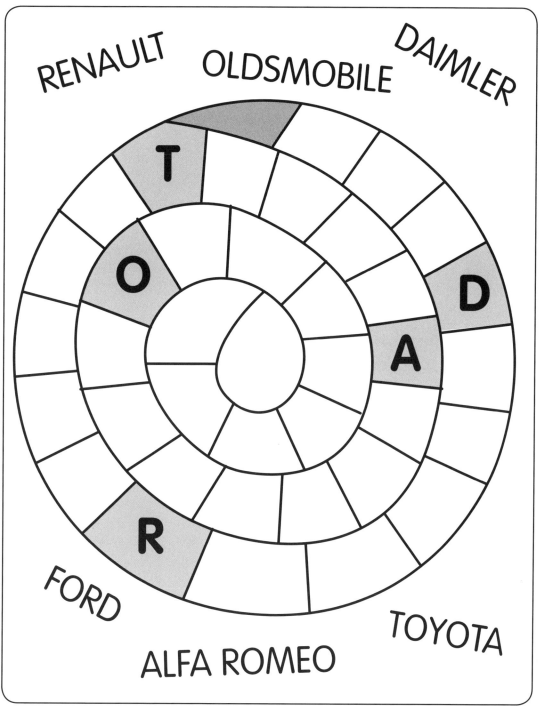

RENAULT OLDSMOBILE DAIMLER

FORD

ALFA ROMEO

TOYOTA

TIME TO FLY!

Don't miss your flight! Match each flight
time to the correct clock.

SUPER STUNTS

Add some eye-catching colours to this stunt bike.

HOT RODS

Do the sums to work out which driver belongs to each car.

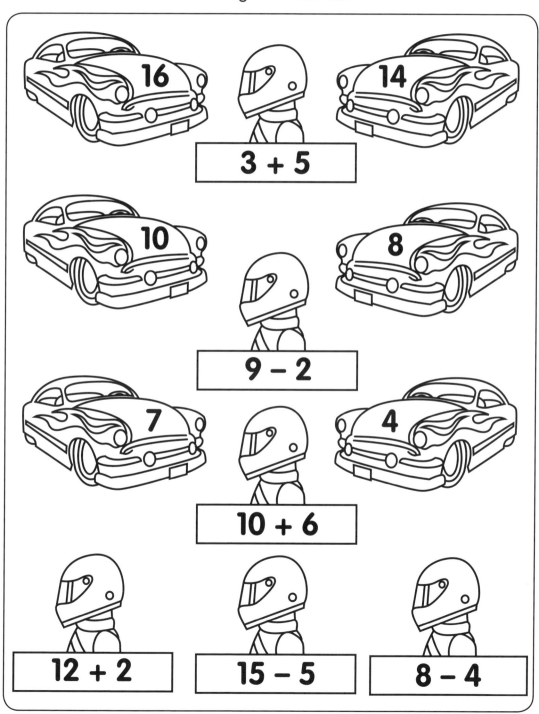

16

14

3 + 5

10

8

9 − 2

7

4

10 + 6

12 + 2

15 − 5

8 − 4

HARVEST TIME

Look carefully to find eight farm vehicles hidden in the grid.

```
C  O  M  B  Y  A  R  P  S  T  I  L
T  B  S  T  A  L  L  E  R  Q  U  A
B  I  A  A  R  O  T  C  A  R  T  Q
Q  A  L  S  R  A  R  O  O  H  T  U
A  U  X  H  E  R  A  I  A  G  R  A
R  Q  A  P  L  P  O  B  T  U  A  D
T  R  A  D  A  S  S  W  I  O  I  O
U  C  O  M  B  I  N  E  L  L  L  B
T  O  T  O  P  I  C  K  U  P  E  A
R  X  L  C  O  P  K  T  C  A  R  T
A  O  S  P  R  A  Y  E  R  Q  U  A
I  Q  W  C  O  M  B  P  L  O  U  G
```

COMBINE
TRAILER
TRACTOR
BALER
PICKUP
PLOUGH
QUAD BIKE
SPRAYER

23

SNOW TIME!

Make this a winter wonderland with a colourful snow mobile.

BLAST OFF!

Which of the rockets has the highest mission number?
Do the sums to find out.

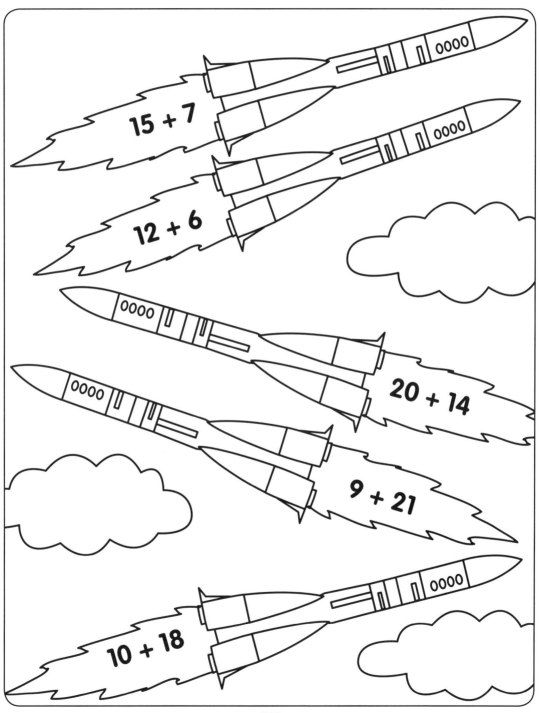

15 + 7

12 + 6

20 + 14

9 + 21

10 + 18

ALL AT SEA

Look at the main picture of the aircraft carrier and then work out which of the smaller pictures is how it would look from above.

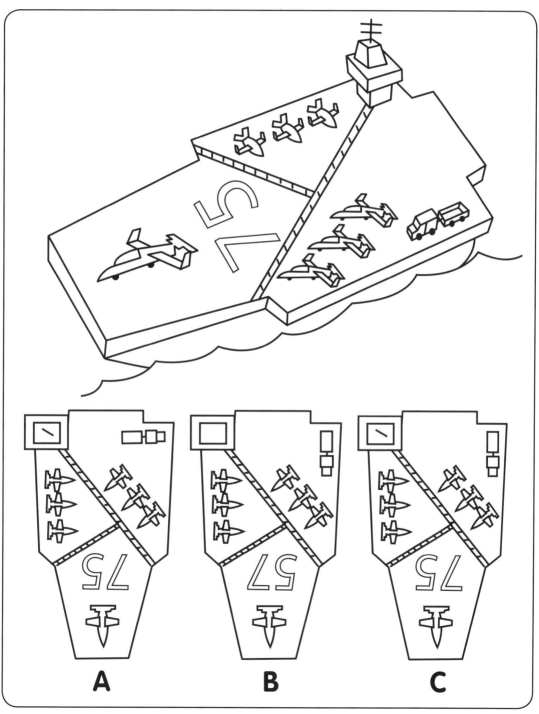

A **B** **C**

DIGGING THE DIRT

Add some colour to this busy scene.

QUICK FIT

Use the clue letters to help you fit the car names in the grid.
If you get them right, the circled letters will spell another car name.

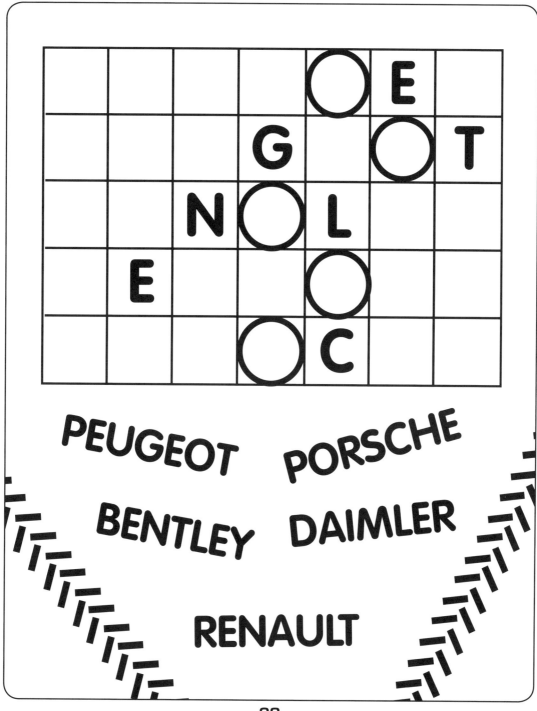

PEUGEOT   PORSCHE

BENTLEY   DAIMLER

RENAULT

COUNTDOWN

Guide the snowmobile through the snowdrifts
by counting down from 8 to 1.

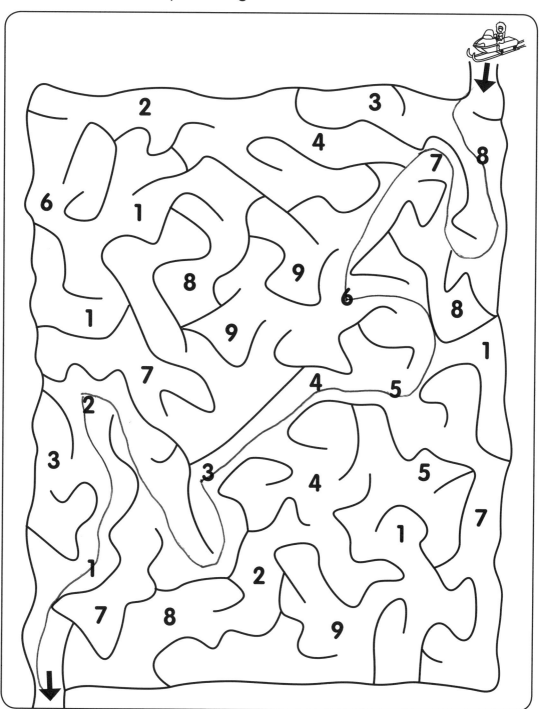

AIRBORNE

What colours do you need for this amazing sky-high view? Colour it in!

BULLET TRAIN

Cross out all of the letters O, T, and R to find a country famous for its high-speed bullet train.

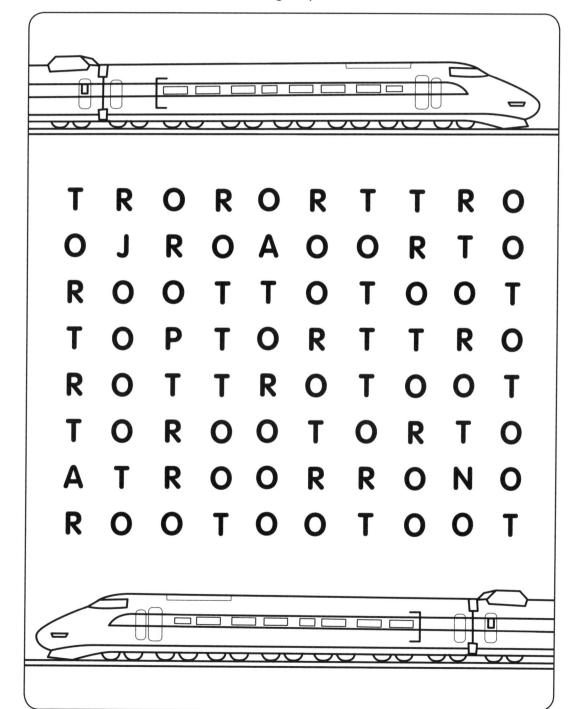

T R O R O R T T R O
O J R O A O O R T O
R O O T T O T O O T
T O P T O R T T R O
R O T T R O T O O T
T O R O O T O R T O
A T R O O R R O N O
R O O T O O T O O T

FINISH LINE

How many smaller words can you make from the letters below?
Two are listed to get you started.

CHEQUERED FLAG

RED

HERE

WE ARE SAILING

Whisk yourself away to a watery world as you colour.

FARES, PLEASE

Look at the bottom bus to find
two extra passengers.

EAT MY DUST

Cross out any double letters to leave the name of
a vehicle that can be fun as well as useful.

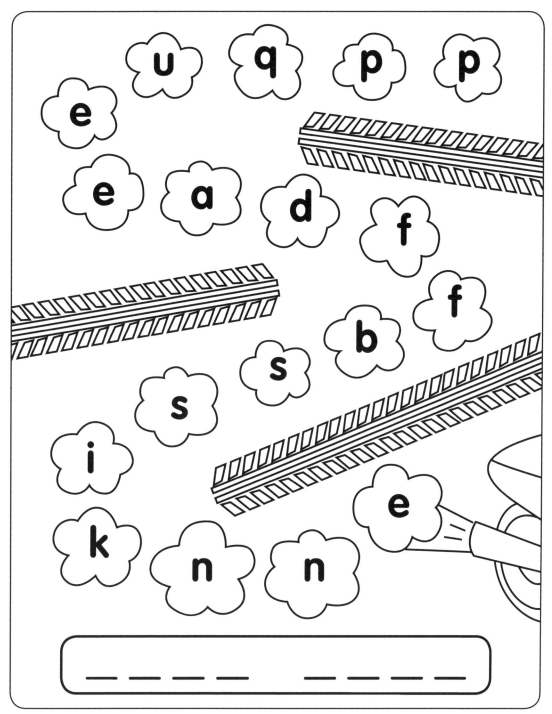

_ _ _ _ _   _ _ _ _

TIPPER TRUCK

Have fun finishing this picture with bright colours.

MINI MATCH

Which two pictures are
exactly the same?

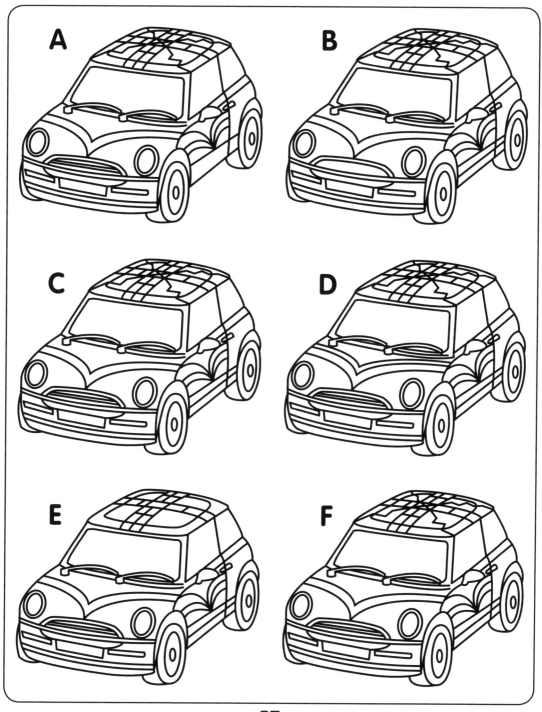

KEEP ON TRUCKING

Can you find the truck driver's name hidden in the grid?
He is called Mike.

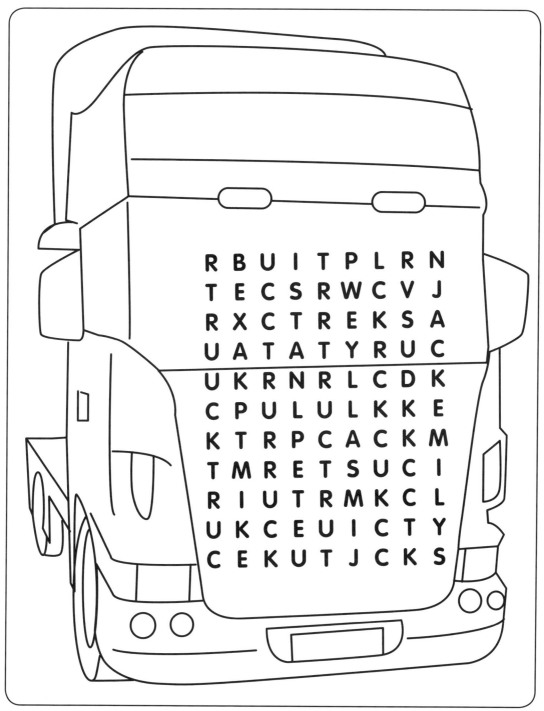

```
R B U I T P L R N
T E C S R W C V J
R X C T R E K S A
U A T A T Y R U C
U K R N R L C D K
C P U L U L K K E
K T R P C A C K M
T M R E T S U C I
R I U T R M K C L
U K C E U I C T Y
C E K U T J C K S
```

SPEED KINGS

Grab your colouring pens and race to finish the picture!

JOIN THE DOTS

Join the dots to find a highly unusual
form of transport!

CHOO CHOO!

Which of the steam trains has travelled the farthest?
Add up the numbers for each to find out.

SETTING SAIL

Colour in this old fashioned ship as it sails the high seas.

MONSTER MAZE

Find a path to get the truck through the maze
and out the other side.

START

FINISH

SAFETY FIRST

Which of the helmets is a tiny bit
different from the others?

ARMY PATROL

Add your best camouflage colours to these army vehicles.

STARTING UP

Rearrange the sets of letters to find which vehicles these keys belong to.

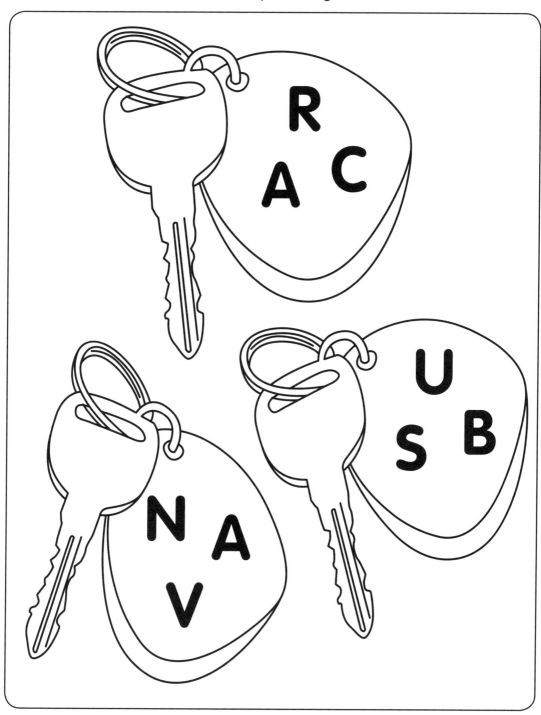

AND THE WINNER IS

Count the stars on each car to find out who comes first,
second, third and fourth in the race.

MAN ON THE MOON

Use space-age colours to make this scene truly out-of-this-world!

SUPERSONIC

Guide the jet plane out of the maze. Avoid the
passenger planes along the way!

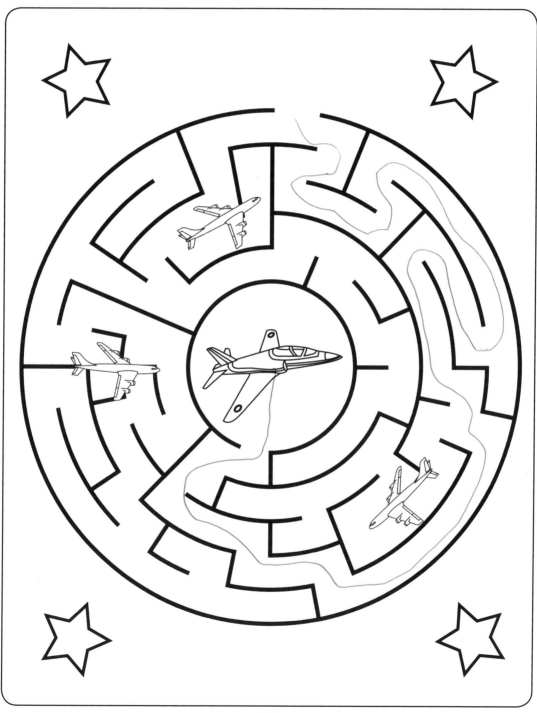

TAKE THE TRAIN

Cross out the double letters to find out
where each train is going.

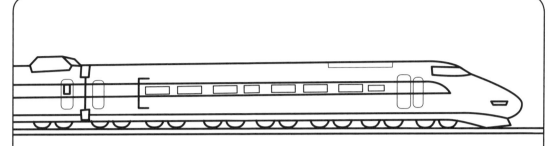

PPBOFFSJJTOHHN

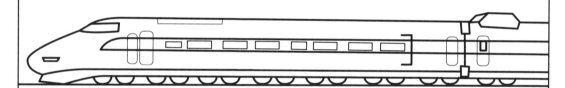

MLLOTTSCEEOWRR

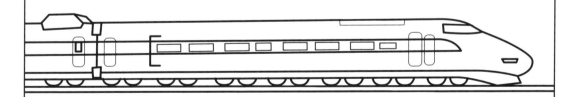

AABPPERGGLOOIN

SPEED OF SOUND

Add your own colour to this supersonic scene.

DISPLAY TEAM

Which of the display riders has something
different about his uniform?

VERY FUNNY

Follow the instructions to find the
answer to the joke.

What did the traffic light say to the car?

BRAIN	STOP	SHUT
WE'LL	DON'T	DRIVE
SOON	BE	TRAIN
LOOK	CRANE	I'M
MAIN	NEAR	SAFE
CHANGING	STATION	HELP

1. Cross out words beginning with S.

2. Delete words that rhyme with 'rain'.

3. Get rid of any word containing E.

MEN AT WORK

What colour will this cement mixer be when you have finished work?

MOUNTAIN TOP

Race up the mountain maze to get to
the cable car at the top.

START

DIRT TRACKS

Cross out every other letter, starting with P,
to find out what has made these tracks.

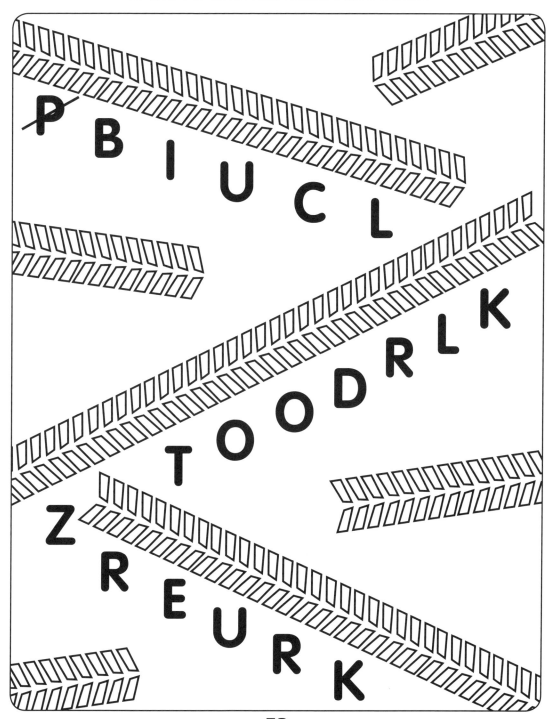

P B I U C L

T O O D R L K

T

Z R E U R K

SUPERSPEED

Fill in this high-speed train with eye-catching colours.

PONY RIDE

Fit the words into the grid and the circled letters
will spell a kind of carriage pulled by a horse.

JEEP

TANK

CART

BOAT

MUD SLIDE

Can you spot six differences between
these two pictures?

EASY RIDER

This chopper is off on a road trip. Add your own custom designs!

SPEED MACHINES

See if you can solve these maths problems without a calculator.

1. If a man goes to buy new tyres for his four motorbikes, how many tyres will he need?

2. A car drives for three hours, travelling at 30 miles an hour. How far does it travel?

3. A train has 14 carriages. Half of them are red and half of them are white. How many red carriages are there?

4. A bus carrying 12 passengers breaks down. The passengers get onto another bus that is passing by, with 7 passengers on it. How many passengers are on the broken down bus?

TRAIN CROSSING

Find a way from the edge of the sign
to the picture in the middle.

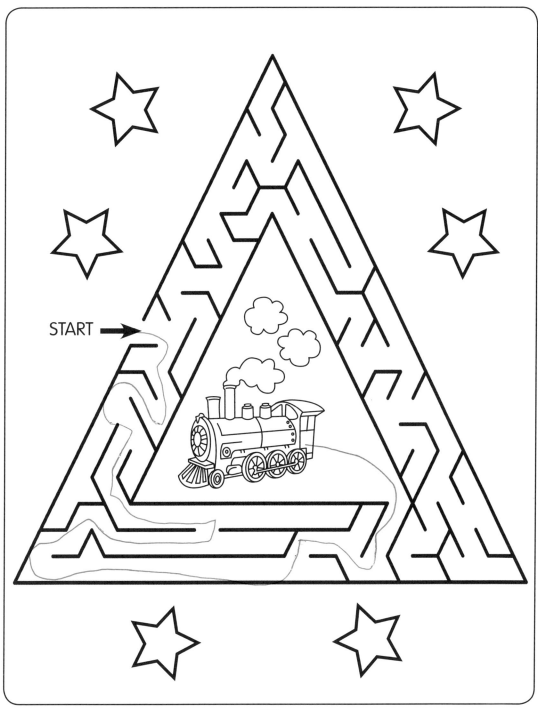

START →

CITY CARS

Add some colour for the drivers of these cars.

ALL MIXED UP

Unscramble the letters to find the name of a job
where you might drive this truck.

E   L   D
  U
R   B
  I

ODD ONE OUT

Which of these vehicles is the odd one out?

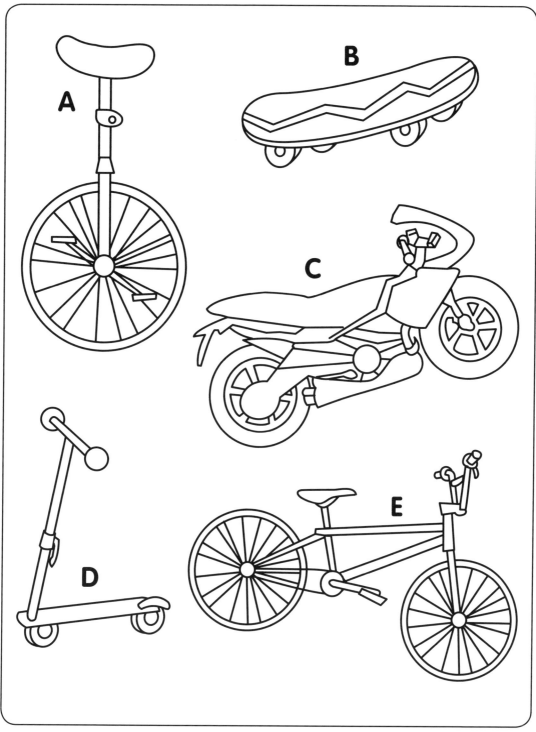

A

B

C

D

E

MEGA MOPED

Brighten up this scene with lots of colour.

TO THE RESCUE

Which of the jigsaw pieces fills the gap?

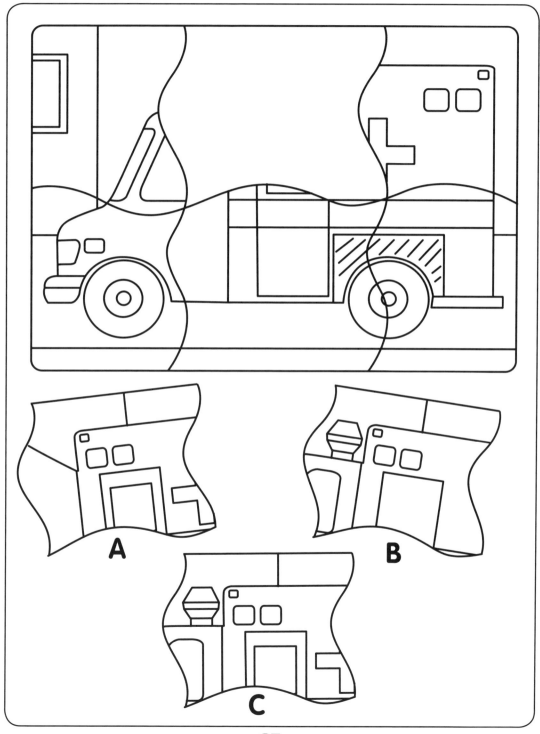

A

B

C

ON TRACK

Look carefully to find six railway words
hidden in the letter grid.

TRAIN

TRACK   STEAM

```
P  A  Y  S  E  L  K  S
R  I  T  R  A  I  N  K
A  E  T  E  G  S  G  H
I  R  C  R  D  T  U  T
L  R  T  A  R  E  A  E
S  V  E  U  T  A  R  R
T  R  A  C  K  M  D  C
L  W  H  E  E  L  E  A
```

WHEEL   GUARD

RAILS

ICE CREAM TIME!

Hurray! Colour the van and the yummy ice creams.

DRIVER DILEMMA

Help the tractor to find a way through the field.

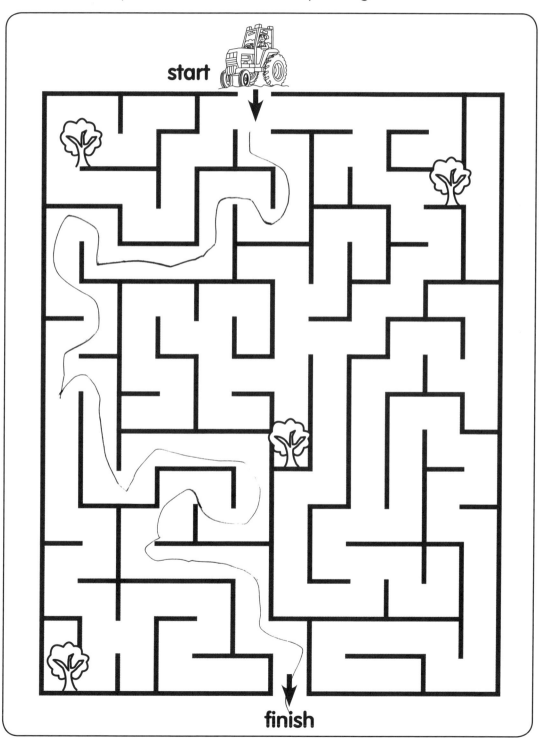

start

finish

PEOPLE CARRIER

Use the letters on vehicles with less than four wheels to spell something that can carry lots of people.

71

SUNNY DAY

Colour in this beautiful sunny sailing scene.

BLACK OUT

Which of the silhouettes is an exact match for the picture of the dune buggy?

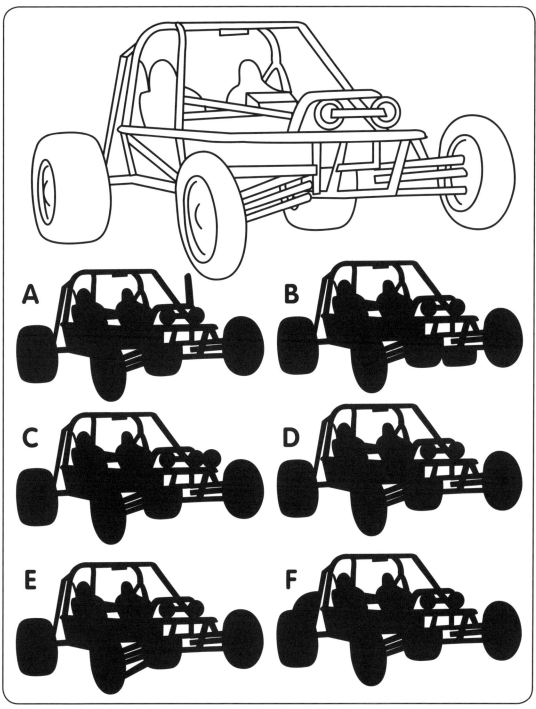

BUILDING SITE

There are six differences between these two pictures.
See if you can spot them all!

AMERICAN CHOPPER

Only two of these bikes are identical.
Can you see which two?

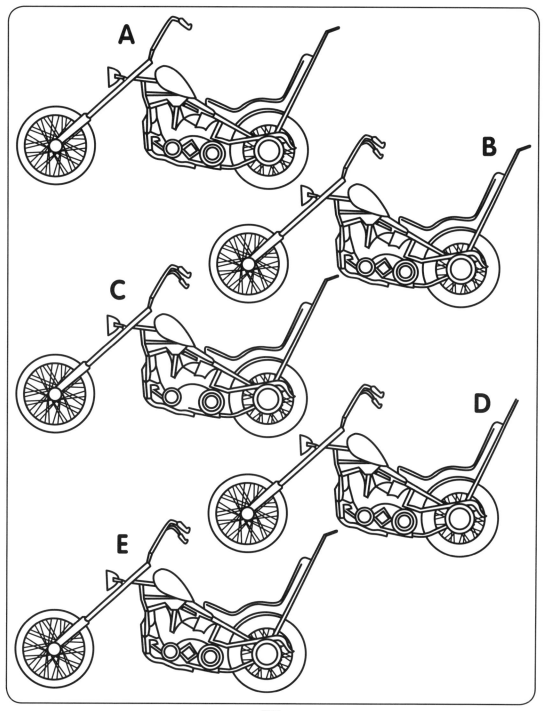

FIRE FIRE!

Add three more to the number each time,
to count up the ladder in threes.

ANSWERS

1. 3

2. B and F

4. 27 18 30 25

5. HAY

7.

9.

```
        S
      S A I
    S A L S A
    A L L A I L
  A S L S A L S L
  S A I A L S A I S
  S S I I L A I S S A
  S I A L S L I S S S I A
A I L S L A I       L S
I L S A I I A L S L I S A
```

10. 2 4 6 8 10 12 14 16 18 20

12.

13.

14. SEA RESCUE

16. C

17.

19. FORD-DAIMLER-RENAULT-
    TOYOTA-ALFA ROMEO-
    OLDSMOBILE

20.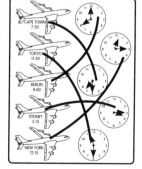

22. 3 + 5 = 8   9 – 2 = 7
    10 + 6 = 16   12 + 2 = 14
    15 – 5 = 10   8 – 4 = 4

23.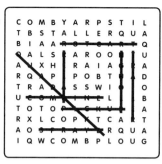

25. 15 + 7 = 22
    12 + 6 = 18
    20 + 14 = 34
    9 + 21 = 30
    10 + 18 = 28

26. C

28. LOTUS

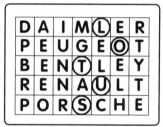

29.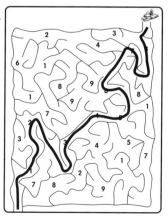

31. JAPAN

32. Here are some you might have found: chef, quad, leg, due, queer, gel, reel, reef, herd, gale.

34.

35. quad bike

37. C and F

38.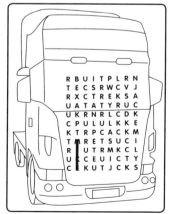

41. A

43.

44.

46. CAR, VAN, BUS

49.

50. BOSTON, MOSCOW, BERLIN

52.

53. Don't look, I'm changing!

55.

56. BULLDOZER

58. TRAP

59.

70.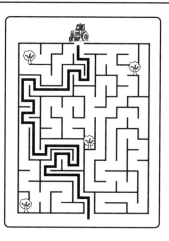

61. 1. 8 2. 90 miles 3. 7
4. None - they all got off!

71. COACH

62.

73. D

74.

64. BUILDER

65. C (the others have no engine)

75. B and E

67. C

76. 3 6 9 12 15 18 21 24

68.
```
P A Y S E L K S
R I T R A I N K
E H E T E G S H
S A R C R D I U
C R L R T A R E
U S V E U T A R
E T R A C K M C
L W H E E L E A
```